A Note to Parents and Teachers

DK READERS is a compelling programme for beginning readers, designed in conjunction with literacy experts, including Maureen Fernandes, B.Ed (Hons). Maureen has spent many years teaching literacy, both in the classroom and as a consultant in schools.

Beautiful illustrations and superb full-colour photographs combine with engaging, easy-to-read stories to offer a fresh approach to each subject in the series.

Each DK READER is guaranteed to capture a child's interest while developing his or her reading skills, general knowledge and love of reading.

The five levels of DK READERS are aimed at different reading abilities, enabling you to choose the books that are exactly right for your child:

Pre-level 1: Learning to read
Level 1: Beginning to read
Level 2: Beginning to read alone
Level 3: Reading alone
Level 4: Proficient readers

The "normal" age at which a child begins to read can be anywhere from three to eight years old. Adult participation through the lower levels is very helpful for providing encouragement, discussing storylines and sounding out unfamiliar words.

No matter which level you select, you can be sure that you are helping your child learn to read, then read to learn!

LONDON, NEW YORK, MUNICH,
MELBOURNE and DELHI

Editor Kate Simkins
Designers Cathy Tincknell
and John Kelly
Senior Editor Catherine Saunders
Brand Manager Lisa Lanzarini
Publishing Manager Simon Beecroft
Category Publisher Alex Allan
Production Editor Siu Chan
Production Controller Amy Bennett

Reading Consultant
Maureen Fernandes

Published in Great Britain in 2008 by
Dorling Kindersley Limited,
80 Strand, London WC2R 0RL

08 09 10 10 9 8 7 6 5 4 3 2 1

A CIP record for this book is available from the British Library.

ISBN: 978-1-4053-2894-4

Hi-res workflow proofed by Media Development and Printing Ltd, UK.
Printed and bound in China by L-Rex Printing Co. Ltd.

Discover more at
www.dk.com

Contents

DK READERS

The SPY-CATCHER GANG

Written by John Kelly
Illustrated by Inklink

DK

THE SPY~CATCHER GANG

Harry's story takes place in London in 1940. At this time, Britain was at war with Adolf Hitler's Nazi Germany. The German Army had taken control of most of western Europe and was now turning its attention to the British Isles. First the German Air Force tried to destroy British airbases, but the RAF fought back in an air battle called the Battle of Britain. Then, in an attack known as the Blitz, the German Air Force began dropping bombs on British cities, including London, Birmingham, Coventry, Liverpool and Belfast. Turn to page 44 to see a map and timeline, then let the story begin....

"My name is Harry Tucker and I am 12 years old. I live in the East End of London with my mum and my baby sister. My dad is away fighting, and I think about him all the time. The German bombs are scary, but it is fun exploring the bombed-out buildings, even if my mum would go mad if she ever found out! I've heard that German spies could be anywhere so I am always on the look out for them."

DID YOU KNOW? "Blitz" means "lightning" in German.

Barrage balloons were put up to stop enemy planes getting too close.

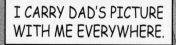
I CARRY DAD'S PICTURE WITH ME EVERYWHERE.

MUM, I WISH I COULD BE A PILOT LIKE DAD AND SHOOT DOWN ENEMY PLANES.

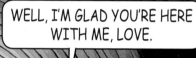
WELL, I'M GLAD YOU'RE HERE WITH ME, LOVE.

I'M NOT SCARED...

...BUT TWO BOYS FROM OUR SCHOOL WERE KILLED LAST WEEK.

IT MAKES YOU WONDER WHO WILL BE NEXT.

DID YOU KNOW? The German Air Force was called the Luftwaffe.

More than a million homes in London were damaged during the bombing. 11

DID YOU KNOW? Many famous London buildings were damaged during the Blitz.

DID YOU KNOW? *Many London children were **evacuated** during the war.*

They were sent to stay with families outside London where it was safer. 15

DID YOU KNOW? Every street had an air raid warden to help during the Blitz.

THE ONLY PLACE WAS THE HOUSE ON WELLINGTON STREET.

I HOPED THEY'D NEVER FIND ME THERE.

CAN YOU SEE THE BOY ANYWHERE?

NO!

DANGER! KEEP OUT!

He or she did many important jobs, including sounding the air raid siren.

DID YOU KNOW? All British men aged between 18 and 41 had to fight.

DID YOU KNOW? Bombs were designed to explode on impact.

But about one in ten bombs did not explode straightaway.

21

DID YOU KNOW? From 1940, the British prime minister was Winston Churchill.

DID YOU KNOW? The worst night of the London Blitz was 10 May 1941.

DID YOU KNOW? *Coventry was one of the most badly bombed British cities.*

· *DID YOU KNOW? During the Blitz, people had to cover their windows and doors.*

DID YOU KNOW? *School pupils had to practise putting on their gas masks.*

When there was an air raid, the whole school took cover in a shelter. 33

DID YOU KNOW? The British government had its own shelter in London.

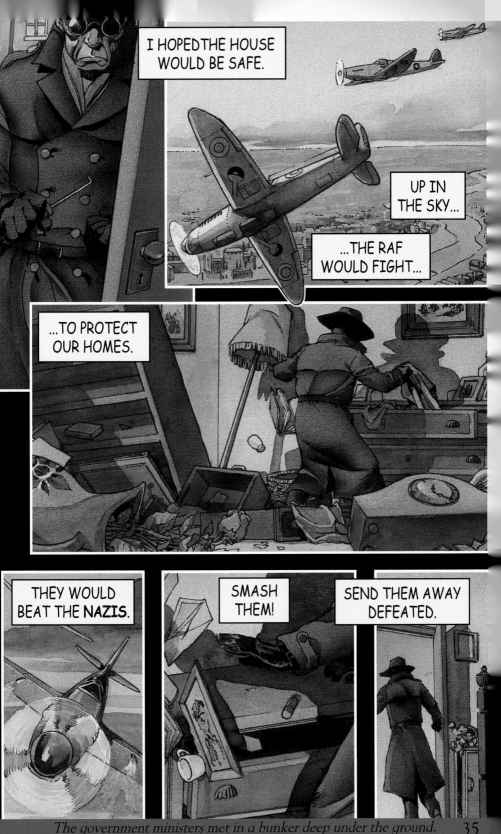

DID YOU KNOW? London Underground stations were popular places to shelter.

DID YOU KNOW? The king and queen stayed in London during the Blitz.

DID YOU KNOW? People were told to "make do and mend" during the war.

This meant they should reuse things instead of throwing them away.

DID YOU KNOW? The Germans surrendered on 8 May 1945.

Many people celebrated on the streets of Britain.

WORLD WAR II

There were two world wars in the 20th century. World War I (1914–1918) ended when Britain, France, the United States and their allies (friends) defeated Germany and its allies. Germany was made to give up land and pay money to the victors. Many Germans resented this. In 1933, Adolf Hitler and his Nazi Party seized power in Germany. The Nazis promised to make Germany a strong nation once again.

World War II started in September 1939, when the German Army invaded Poland. France and Britain (the Allies) then declared war on Germany. After many fierce battles, the Germans took control of most of western Europe. Hitler then prepared to invade the British Isles. In 1940, the German Air Force began bombing British cities in an attempt to make Britain surrender.

Germany attacked Russia in 1941, so the Russians joined the war on the side of the Allies. Germany, Italy and Japan formed an alliance (the Axis). In 1941, Japan bombed US ships in Pearl Harbor, Hawaii, bringing the Americans into the war. Soon, there was fighting all over the globe. The war in Europe ended when Allied troops invaded Germany in May 1945. Japan surrendered in August 1945.

A map of Europe in 1942. Most of Europe and some of North Africa were occupied by Axis troops.

44

Mount Everest climbed for first time

US astronauts land on the Moon | 1969

South Africa's Nelson Mandela released from prison | 1990

953

TIMELINE

1960

1980

2000

GLOSSARY

LONDON   PAGE 5

London is a city in southern England and is the capital of the United Kingdom.

RAF   PAGE 5

"RAF" stands for the "Royal Air Force", which is the British Air Force. In World War II, RAF planes defended the skies above Britain from German planes and also dropped bombs on enemy cities.

AIR RAID SIRENS   PAGE 6

Air raid sirens were machines that made a loud wailing noise – loud enough to wake people up if they were asleep. The sirens told people that there were enemy planes on the way and that they should go to a shelter.

SHELTER   PAGE 6

An air raid shelter was a place that people could go where they would be safe from the bombs. Many people had Anderson shelters in their gardens. These temporary shelters were made of curved panels of steel that joined together to form the roof and sides. Some people had small steel shelters in their homes and others sheltered in London Underground stations.

BOMBED   PAGE 6

German planes started dropping bombs (metal cases full of explosives) on London on 7 September 1940. They bombed the city almost every night or day until 10 May 1941.

GERMAN PLANE   PAGE 7

The German planes that dropped bombs on British cities were mainly a type called Heinkel bombers.

BARRAGE BALLOONS   PAGE 7

These large balloons were attached to the ground by steel cables. They were designed to prevent enemy planes getting too close to the ground.

SEARCHLIGHTS   PAGE 9

From the ground, British soldiers shone beams of light from huge lamps called searchlights onto German planes. This made the planes easier for the soldiers to see and shoot at.

GUNS   PAGE 9

Anti-aircraft guns on the ground fired at enemy planes.

BBC   PAGE 10

"BBC" stands for the "British Broadcasting Corporation". During World War II, most people listened to the BBC radio for news about the war. The BBC also made television programmes, but few people had television sets at this time.

EAST END DOCKS   PAGE 10

The large area in the east of London is commonly known as the East End. During World War II, the East End docks (where ships were loaded and unloaded) were often the targets of bombing raids. Most people living in the East End during the war were fairly poor and worked in factories or at the docks. Because family and friends all lived in the same area, people could look after each other during the terrible times of the Blitz.

SHRAPNEL   PAGE 11

Pieces of metal thrown out by a bomb when it explodes.

BOMB SITES   PAGE 11

Places where bombs have exploded and destroyed the buildings.

SPY PAGE 23

A spy is someone who finds out secret information. During World War II, the British government warned people not to talk to strangers in case they were German spies and to be careful what they said in public.

DETECTIVE SERGEANT PAGE 32

A detective sergeant is a British police officer who tries to solve major crimes. He does not wear a uniform.

NAZIS PAGE 35

The Nazis were a group of people, led by Adolf Hitler, who ruled Germany from 1933 to 1945. They believed that the Germans were better than any other race and that many of Gemany's problems were caused by Jews.

LOOTERS PAGE 36

Looters are people who steal from houses and shops in wartime or during riots.

UNDERGROUND PAGE 37

The railway that travels beneath London's streets is called the Underground or the tube. During the war, people took shelter on the station platforms and often stayed there all night.

RUBBLE PAGE 40

Piles of broken pieces from buildings that have been blown up.

GAS LEAK PAGE 40

Gas is a fuel that is used mainly for cooking and heating. It is invisible but easily set on fire, and if any gas escapes from a pipe, it may cause an explosion.

SPIV PAGE 41

Spivs were people who stole rationed goods and sold them to people at high prices, especially during and just after World War II. This was against the law, but many people bought from spivs because they couldn't get what they needed any other way. The buying and selling of illegal goods is called the black market.

GAS MAIN PAGE 42

A gas main is a large pipe that carries gas to a street of houses.

GAS MASK PAGE 12

A gas mask is worn over the face to stop the wearer from breathing in poisonous gas. During World War II, every person in Britain had to carry a gas mask to protect them from poison gas attacks by the Germans, although there were actually no gas attacks in World War II.

EVACUATED PAGE 14

Sent away from a place of danger.

IDENTITY CARDS PAGE 19

When the war started in 1939, the British government decided that everyone should carry identity cards. The cards had information about each person, including his or her name and address.

RATION BOOKS PAGE 19

During the war, ships bringing things such as food and clothes to Britain were attacked. This meant that many things started to run out, so to make sure everyone got their share, the government gave every family a ration book. Each book contained coupons that people could use in shops in exchange for clothes and essential foods such as butter, milk, eggs, sugar and meat.

BOMB DISPOSAL OFFICER PAGE 20

Any bombs that did not explode when they hit the ground had to be made safe. This was the job of the bomb disposal officers, who were specially trained soldiers.

DEFUSING PAGE 20

Bombs contain fuses – switches that make the bomb explode. The fuse has to be removed to make the bomb safe. This is called defusing.